かみさまに
うたえるようにしていただいた

キャドモンさん
Mr Cadmon

Mr Cadmon who was given a gift of singing

ぶん）はまじま　びん
え）　みのわ　まりこ

Bin Hamajima
Mariko Minowa

22世紀アート

本書を読んでくださる皆様へ

　私は、ずっと聖書に関わり、特に研究の一環として、聖書翻訳の研究をしてきました。そして一つ一つの翻訳の背後に、素晴らしいエピソードがあることを感じていました。聖書そのものの素晴らしさはもちろんですが、それを民衆に与えるために努力した人々、中には、そのために自分の命さえ捧げた人たちがいます。それらの人たちに関する本を数冊執筆、また翻訳してきました。それで、このような素晴らしい人たちのことを子供たちにもぜひ知ってほしいと思いました。絵本であればそれを読んでくださるご両親にも同時に知っていただくことができます。そして、この企画をしました。前期１０冊、後期１０冊ほどの絵本シリーズにしたいと願っています。

　絵を描いてくださる方をずっと求めていましたが、幸い箕輪まり子様という素晴らしい方を紹介していただきました。私と思いを共有していただき、素晴らしい絵を描いていただきました。私の思いを超えた綺麗で温かい絵です。きっと子供たちばかりでなく、大人の人たちにも多くの感動を与えてくれると信じています。何よりも、このシリーズが、読む人を感動させ、神様に栄光を帰することが、私たちの最も希望するところです。

浜島　敏

Dear readers,

I have been involved with the Bible for a very long time. In particular, I have been studying Bible translations as part of my research. And I have got the impression that there is a wonderful story behind each and every translation. The Bible itself is of course a wonderful book, but there are also a great many people who have worked very hard to bring it to the masses, some of whom have even given up their lives for this purpose. I have written and translated several books on such figures, and I wanted children to know about these wonderful people as well. I realised that writing a picture book would be a great way to have the parents learn their lives as well, as they read the story to thier children.

I had been looking for someone to do the illustrations for a long time, and I was fortunate enough to be introduced to a wonderful person, Ms Mariko Minowa. She shared my feelings and created wonderful illustrations. Her illustrations are warmer and more beautiful than I could have ever hoped for. I am convinced that they have the power to move and impress both children and adults alike. Our greatest hope is that this series will inspire those who read it and bring glory to God.

Bin Hamajima

イギリスの　あるまちに

キャドモンさんと

いうひとが　いました

キャドモンさんは

しゅうどういんの

うしのせわを　していました

On the hill of a little town of

Whitby in northern England,

there was a man named Mr Cadmon.

Mr Cadmon was taking care

of cows in the abbey.

キャドモンさんは

かみさまが　だいすきでした

でも　うたが　うたえませんでした

だいすきなかみさまを

さんびすることができなくて

とても　さびしかったのです

しゅうどういんでは　ゆうしょくのあと

みんなで　かわるがわる

たのしく　うたをうたいました

Mr Cadmon loved God,

but he couldn' t sing.

He was very sad because

he could not sing

praises to God he loved so much.

At Whitby Abbey, after dinner,

everyone used to

take turns singing songs.

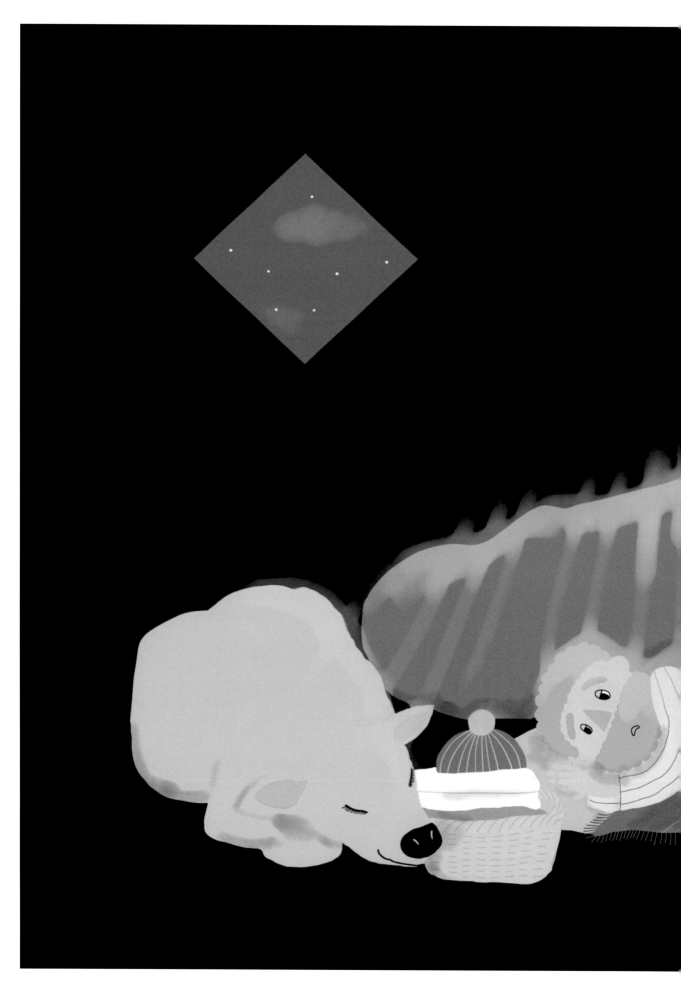

キャドモンさんは
じぶんの　ばんが　ちかづくと
こそこそと　しょくどうを
でていきました
そして　うしごやで
うしといっしょに　ねるのです

When it was his turn to sing,

Mr Cadmon sneaked

out of the dining room.

He would then go to sleep

with cows in the cowshed.

そんなあるよるのことです
いつものように　キャドモンさんが
ひとり　うしごやにかえって　ねていると
てんから　こえがきこえました
「キャドモンさん　うたってください」

Then one night, as usual,

Mr Cadmon was sleeping alone

in the cowshed.

A voice came from above.

"Mr Cadmon, sing!"

キャドモンさんは

びっくりして　いいました

「かみさま　でも　わたしは　うたえません」

「いいから　わたしのために　うたいなさい」

「なにを　うたったら　いいのですか」

「てんちそうぞうの　うたを」

キャドモンさんは　おそるおそる

こえを　だしてみました

ふしぎやふしぎ　じぶんでもびっくり

するような　きれいなこえがでました

そして　てんとちを　つくって

くださった　かみさまを　たたえました

Mr Cadmon was startled and said,

"My Lord, I can' t sing."

"You sing for me!"

"What should I sing?"

"Sing of the Creation of the World!"

Mr Cadmon, wondering,

opened his mouth to sing.

And lo and behold,

he could sing with the sweetest voice

he had ever heard.

He could sing to God

about the Creation of heaven and earth.

うれしくなった　キャドモンさんは

つぎのあさ　おきてから

ゆめではないかと　しんぱいになって

もういちどうたってみました

ゆうべと　おなじように　うたえました

ぜんぶ　おぼえていたのです

The next morning,

when he woke up,

he was worried that it was only a dream.

So he sang it again.

He could sing the same song as last night.

He remembered everything.

キャドモンさんは
そのことを　しゅうどういんの
いんちょうさんに　はなしました
いんちょうさんは
キャドモンさんが　うたえるように
してくださったのは
かみさまだと　わかりました

Mr Cadmon told this

to the abbess of the abbey.

The abbess realised that

it was God who had enabled him to sing.

それから　キャドモンさんは

まいにち　せいしょの

おはなしを　きいて

そのおはなしを　うたにしました

From that day on,

Mr Cadmon was taught

Bible stories every day,

and he sang them into songs.

そして　みんなに
かみさまのことを　つたえました
うしかいキャドモンさんは
いまでは　かみさまを　さんびする
キャドモンさんと　なりました

In this way,

he told the people about God,

the Creator of the world.

Once cow-raising Mr Cadmon has now

become God-praising Mr Cadmon.

保護者の皆様、教会学校の先生方へ

　キャドモンの生まれた年はよくわかっていませんが、およそ七世紀の中ごろに活躍した人で、670 から 680 年ころに亡くなっています。イギリスの東海岸にあるウィトビーという場所に、修道院が出来、そこの牛飼いをしていたのが、キャドモンです。しかし、本文に書いたように、あるとき、突然、歌の賜物が与えられて、聖書の天地創造から、出エジプト、さらに新約のイエス伝、その死と復活、使徒たちの働き、そして、最後の審判にいたるまでの聖書全体の物語をアングロ・サクソンの詩の形式で伝えたと、伝えられています。キャドモンの死後、50 年ほど後の、ビードという歴史家がそのことを伝えています。彼の書いた詩は、ほとんど残っていませんが、創世記の冒頭の「神は天と地を創造した」という部分を次のような詩にしています。

いざ讃えん	天つみ国の護り主を
造り主の力	神の思慮
栄光の父のみ業を	永遠の君
もろもろの希しきわざの	基定めしを。
そははじめ、	地の子らのため、
屋根として天を造れり、	聖なる造り主は、

（鈴木重威・鈴木もと子共訳『古代英詩』より引用）

　昔のイギリスに住んでいたケルト人の中には、バードと呼ばれる吟遊詩人がいて、リュートという名の楽器の伴奏で英雄物語を伝えていました。日本の「琵琶法師」のような人だと考えて良いと思います。そのような人がクリスチャンになって、聖書物語を伝えるようになったと言われています。ひょっとして、キャドモンは、そのような人の一人かも知れません。日本でも、琵琶法師や講談師とか浪曲師がキリスト伝を伝えたら、もっと日本に聖書物語が浸透したのではないかと思ったりします。ロンドンのウェストミンスター寺院の中の詩人のコーナーに最初の詩人として記念されています。またウィトビーの海岸に近い高台に今も大きな修道院の跡が残っています。そしてキャドモンを記念する十字架が建っています。

To Parents and Sunday School Teachers

The year of Cadmon's birth is not known, but he was active in the middle of the 7th century and died between 670 and 680. Cadmon was a cowherd at Whitby abbey on the east coast of England. As mentioned in the text, Cadmon was suddenly given the gift of song, and he is said to have told the entire biblical story in Anglo-Saxon verse, from the creation to the Exodus, the New Testament story of Jesus: his death and resurrection, the apostles' ministry, and the Last Judgement. About 50 years after Cadmon's death, a historian named Bede tells us that. Although only very little of his poetry remains, he is believed to have written the following poem (quoted in Bede' s History) from the opening lines of Genesis 1:1, "God created the heaven and the earth."

Now let us praise the power of the Creator

the glorious work of the Father of all His wonderful works.

In the beginning   He made the heavens as a roof

the protector of the kingdom of heaven.

Thought of God   Eternal Lord

For the children of the earth   The Holy Maker.

Among the Celts who lived in old times in Britain, there were bards, (or minstrels), who told heroic tales to the accompaniment of a musical instrument called the lute. They could be compared to as "biwa-hoshi" in Japan. When bards became Christian, they began to tell biblical stories. Perhaps Cadmon was one of such people. Cadmon is commemorated in the Poet's Corner of Westminster Abbey in London as the first English poet. The ruin of a large monastery remains on a hill near the beach at Whitby. A cross stands commemorating Cadmon.

【著者】

浜島敏（はまじま　びん）、愛知県出身、明治学院大学大学院修了。

四国学院大学名誉教授。言語学、聖書翻訳研究。

会員：善通寺バプテスト教会、国際景教研究会、日本国際ギデオン協会ほか。

【イラストレーター】

箕輪まり子（みのわ　まりこ）、東京都出身、

Instagram：https://instagram.com/waawa.maricoool?igshid
=OGQ5ZDc2ODk2ZA==

会員：日本ホーリネス教団池の上キリスト教会。

【Author】

HAMAJIMA, Bin, M.A./ Th.D.; born in Aichi; Professor Emeritus
of Shikoku Gakuin University; member: Zentsuji Baptist
Church; Society of Jingjian Religion, Gideons International.

【Illustrator】

MINOWA, Mariko, born in Tokyo,

Instagram：https://instagram.com/waawa.maricoool?igshid
=OGQ5ZDc2ODk2ZA==

Ikenoue Christian Church.

かみさまにうたえるようにしていただいた
キャドモンさん

2023年6月30日発行　　　　文　　はまじま びん

絵　　みのわ まりこ

発行者　　向 田 翔 一

発行所　　株式会社 22 世紀アート

〒103-0007

東京都中央区日本橋浜町 3-23-1-5F

電話　03-5941-9774

Email: info@22art.net　ホームページ：www.22art.net

発売元　　株式会社日興企画

〒104-0032

東京都中央区八丁堀 4-11-10 第 2SS ビル 6F

電話　03-6262-8127

Email: support@nikko-kikaku.com

ホームページ：https://nikko-kikaku.com/

印刷
製本　　株式会社 PUBFUN

ISBN : 978-4-88877-222-8